GW00854932

Disney · PIXAR

Cars

PaRRagon

Bath · New York · Singapore · Hong Kong · Cologne · Delhi
Melbourne · Amsterdam · Johannesburg · Auckland · Shenzhen

Lightning McQueen dreams of winning the Piston Cup.

The reporters love Lightning McQueen!

The King gets ready for the
tie-breaker race, which will be held in Los Angeles.

Mack, Lightning's loyal driver, is trying to stay awake
on the long drive to California.

Oh, no! Lightning has been bumped loose from Mack!

Lightning McQueen gets himself tangled in telephone wires.

Oh no! Lightning McQueen has been impounded.

Sally convinces Doc that Lightning should stay and repair the road.

Doc will make sure Lightning McQueen fixes the road properly.

Lightning McQueen discovers Doc's Piston Cup.

Sally and Lightning go for a
drive together.

Lightning wants to learn all of Doc's racing tricks. But Doc doesn't want to talk about it.

Everyone in Radiator Springs loves the new,
smooth road!

Lightning McQueen helps The King
to cross the finish line.

Back in Radiator Springs, Lightning McQueen and Sally take another drive together.

Mater and Lightning are on a plane, traveling to Japan,
for the first race of the World Grand Prix.

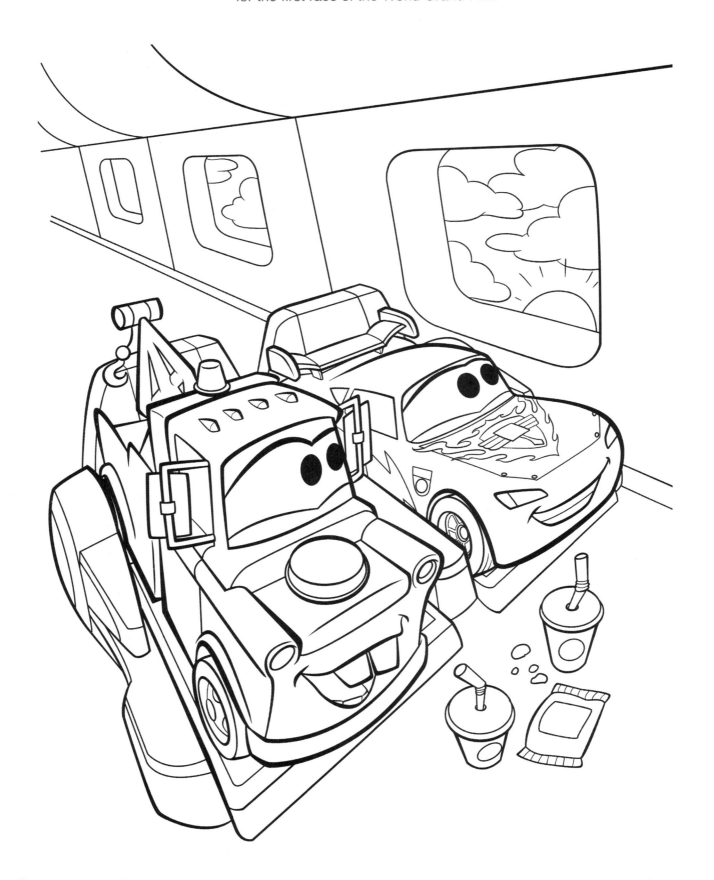

Finn McMissile is looking for an American
agent who has important information to pass on.

Holley Shiftwell is a British secret agent from the
Tokyo office. She is helping Finn on his mission.

Holley mistakes Mater for a secret agent - Mater thinks she wants a date!

The first race of the World Grand Prix has started!

Oh, no! Lightning swerves all over the track. He heard Mater speaking
on his headset and thought his friend was giving him racing tips.

Mater accidentally made Lightning
lose the first race to Francesco Bernoulli.

Siddeley, the spy plane, swoops in for the rescue.

The team makes a stop in Guido and Luigi's hometown.

Mater tries on different disguises.

Lightning and Francesco prepare for the second race of the
World Grand Prix. Lightning really misses Mater.

Lightning zooms ahead and wins the second race of the World Grand Prix.

Holley escapes from her ropes, transforms into a plane, and smashes out of Big Bentley.

Because of his heroic service, the Queen knights Mater.

Mater gets to keep his spy rockets! He and
Lightning blast off down the racetrack together.